I will not sing alone

I will not sing alone

Songs for the seasons of love

John L. Bell

WILD GOOSE PUBLICATIONS

First published 2004

ISBN 1 901557 91 X

Published by Wild Goose Publications
Fourth Floor, Savoy House, 140 Sauchiehall Street, Glasgow G2 3DH, UK
www.ionabooks.com

Wild Goose Publications is the publishing division of the Iona Community.
Scottish Charity No. SC003794.
Limited Company Reg.No. SC0096243.

Cover & design: Graham Maule © 2004 Wild Goose Resource Group

Distributed in Australia by Willow Connection Pty Ltd,
Unit 4A, 3-9 Kenneth Road, Manly Vale NSW 2093, Australia,
and in New Zealand by Pleroma Christian Supplies, Higginson Street,
Otane 4170, Central Hawkes Bay, New Zealand.

A catalogue record for this book is available from the British Library.

Printed by Bell & Bain, Thornliebank, Glasgow, UK

Contents

Introduction

I WILL NOT SING ALONE is a deliberately eclectic collection of words and music from different ages fused in contemporary arrangements.

There are ancient texts and modern texts, simple and sophisticated. There are choral anthems, folk tunes and contemporary syncopated melodies. The songs include exclamations of praise, meditative reflections on the love of God, and laments for the loss of a child and for countries at war.

These are songs of faith which are intended for everybody: not a high octane choral collection or a selection of psuedo-celtic escapist ditties, but songs of engagement with life and with God, all grounded in the passion and pain of Christian love.

All the songs in this collection have also been released on a CD of the same name, recorded by the Wild Goose Collective (an ad hoc collection of ex-Wild Goose Worship Group members and other collaborators) and the Macappella Ceilidh Band. (Catalogue number IC/WGP 034.)

John L. Bell
January 2005

The songs

The Lord is my light

Tune: 'LUX MEA', John L. Bell

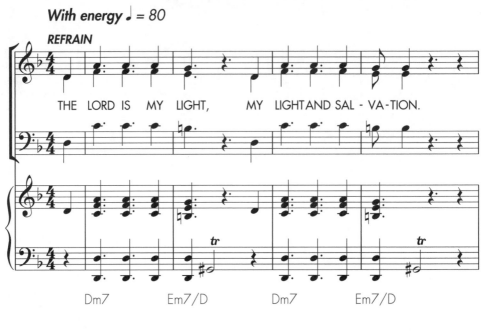

LORD IS MY LIGHT, MY LIGHT AND SAL - VA - TION.

Dm7   Em7/D   Dm7   Em7/D

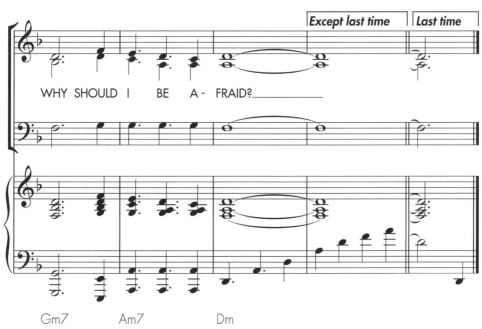

Except last time | *Last time*

WHY SHOULD I BE A - FRAID?_____

Gm7   Am7   Dm

Verse 1

When the powers of e-vil move to-wards me,____

Bb   C

when my ve-ry flesh is un-der threat,

Am   Bb

when my e-ne-mies smell the scent of vict'-ry they shall

Gm7   Gm7/E

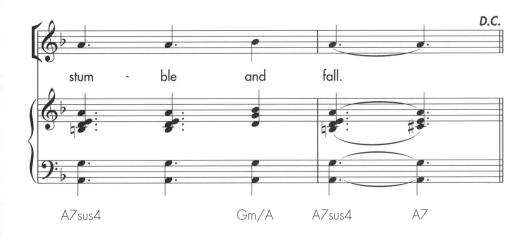

stum - ble and fall.

A7sus4 Gm/A A7sus4 A7

Chorus:
THE LORD IS MY LIGHT, MY LIGHT AND SALVATION.
WHOM SHALL I FEAR, WHOM SHALL I FEAR?
THE LORD IS MY LIGHT, MY LIGHT AND SALVATION.
WHY SHOULD I BE AFRAID?

1.
When the powers of evil move towards me,
when my very flesh is under threat,
when my enemies smell the scent of victory
they shall stumble and fall.

2.
Should a mighty army camp around me,
still my heart would register no fear.
Though a war were waged, though it raged against me
I'd trust God and stand firm.

(continued)

3.
One thing through it all my soul is seeking:
to live all my life within God's house;
there to spend my days, gazing at God's beauty
while at one with my Lord.

4.
God protects me in the time of trouble,
shelters me yet sets me on a rock.
Safe from every harm, safe from all that threatens
I will sing and rejoice.

Psalm 27 on which this text is based is a great song of praise and defiant faith. It deserves more than a limp metrical tune or an ethereal chant. It needs to be gutsy. This should be sung in such a fashion and, if the average pianist can't manage all the notes in the verse, s/he should amend to suit the flexibility of the fingers.

How can I keep from singing?

Tune: 'HOW CAN I KEEP FROM SINGING?', R.Lowry

Firmly ♩ = 80

1. My life flows on in end-less song a-bove earth's la-men-ta-tion. I

catch the sweet, though far off, hymn that hails a new cre-a-tion. NO

STORM CAN SHAKE MY IN-MOST CALM WHILE TO THAT ROCK I'M

Words & melody Robert Lowry (1826-99). Arrangement John L. Bell, copyright © 2005 WGRG, Iona Community, Glasgow G2 3DH, Scotland.

1.
My life flows on in endless song
above earth's lamentation.
I catch the sweet, though far off, hymn
that hails a new creation.

Refrain:
NO STORM CAN SHAKE MY INMOST CALM
WHILE TO THAT ROCK I'M CLINGING.
SINCE LOVE IS LORD OF HEAVEN AND EARTH,
HOW CAN I KEEP FROM SINGING?

2.
Through all the tumult and the strife,
I hear that music ringing.
It finds an echo in my soul.
How can I keep from singing?

(continued)

3.
What though the joys and comforts die?
The Lord my Saviour liveth.
What though the darkness round me close?
Songs in the night he giveth.

4.
The peace of Christ makes fresh my heart,
a fountain ever springing.
All things are mine since I am his!
How can I keep from singing?

This may be an early 19th century American folk hymn, or it might for the greater part be a words and music composition of Robert Lowry (1826-1899). Whatever its origins, it resonates with and for those from St Paul onwards who sang their faith in the face of the powers of darkness. As with all folk and folk-like melodies, the chances of everyone singing the tune the same way are highly unlikely. As with the English tune 'O Waly Waly', several 'original' versions have been attributed to it.

The treasure

Tune: 'THE LICHTBOB'S LASSIE', Scots traditional

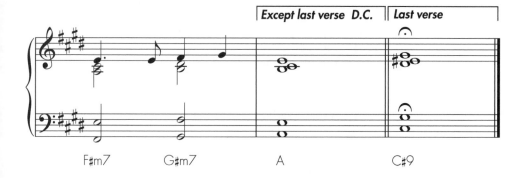

21

1.
If I bought a field
with holy, hidden treasure
buried by the Lord,
and precious beyond measure,

2.
what would I presume
that God, in love, had hidden:
gifts from sages kept
and to the rich forbidden?

3.
Would I think that gold
was what the Lord had planted?
Or might it be the wealth
which all my life I'd wanted?

4.
Or might God conceal
delights I never heeded –
not the things I want,
but what I've always needed?

(continued)

5.
If I bought that field
and found the hidden treasure
would I clutch it tight
or share for others' pleasure?

6.
'Listen' says the Lord,
'the field was long since given.
Treasure lies within;
your heart was sown in heaven.'

Based on one of Jesus' shorter parables (Matthew 13 v 44) and set to the Scottish folk tune 'The Lichtbob's Lassie', this song articulates one of the forgotten yet basic truths of faith: Christ did not come to bring something extra into the world, he came to summon to life that which God had already intended and sown.

Were I the perfect child

Tune : 'O GIN I WERE A BARON'S HEIR', Joseph William Holder, 1765–1823

Moderato ♩ = 60

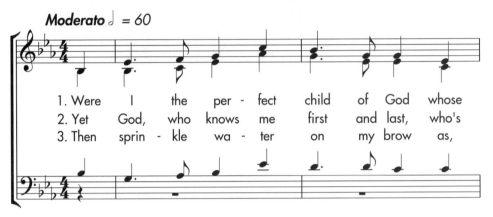

1. Were   I   the   per - fect   child   of   God   whose
2. Yet   God,   who   knows   me   first   and   last,   who's
3. Then   sprin - kle   wa - ter   on   my   brow   as,

faith   was   deep   and   love   was   broad,   not
seen   my   best,   my   worst,   my   past,   has
in   this   place,   I   make   my   vow   to

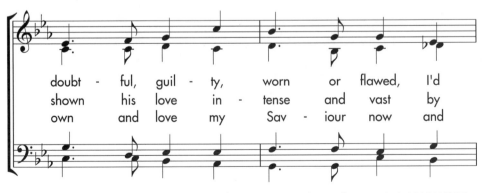

doubt - ful,   guil - ty,   worn   or   flawed,   I'd
shown   his   love   in - tense   and   vast   by
own   and   love   my   Sav - iour   now   and

Melody Joseph William Holder (1765–1823). Words & arrangement John L. Bell, copyright © 2005 WGRG, Iona Community, Glasgow G2 3DH, Scotland.

gladly follow Jesus. But
meeting me in Jesus. For
give myself to Jesus. God

I'm the child of what I've been, es -
Christ, though killed at Calvary by
grant me what I still require that

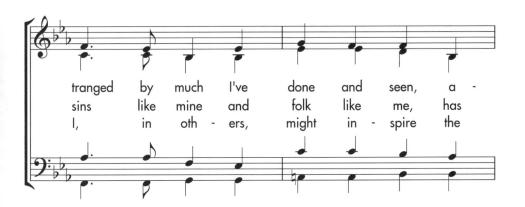

tranged by much I've done and seen, a -
sins like mine and folk like me, has
I, in others, might inspire the

1.
Were I the perfect child of God
whose faith was deep and love was broad,
not doubtful, guilty, worn or flawed,
I'd gladly follow Jesus.
But I'm the child of what I've been
estranged by much I've done and seen,
afraid to show the love I mean,
unfit to follow Jesus.

2.
Yet God, who knows me first and last,
who's seen my best, my worst, my past,
has shown his love intense and vast
by meeting me in Jesus.
For Christ, though killed at Calvary
by sins like mine and folk like me
has risen, forgiven and set me free,
made fit to follow Jesus.

3.
Then sprinkle water on my brow
as, in this place, I make my vow
to own and love my Saviour now
and give myself to Jesus.
God grant me what I still require
that I, in others, might inspire
the hidden hope, the deep desire
to love and follow Jesus.

Verse 3: alternative first 4 lines:

Let all stand witness to my vow
to own and love my saviour now.
and through this water, God allow
my life to be like Jesus.

The Scottish folk song which normally accompanies this tune has a text which is not incomparable to the above. It muses, 'O gin (if) I were a baron's heir', but the possibility of being one is clearly a vacuous hope; whereas the possibility of being counted the perfect child of God is one of the promises of the Gospel.

I will give what I have

Tune: 'DE WILLE', John L. Bell

From a high, sec-ret shelf, I take what I hid my-self - per-fume, pre-cious and rare, nev-er meant to spill or spare. This I'll care-ful-ly break, this I'll emp-ty for his sake: I will

give what I have to my Lord.

1.

From a high, secret shelf, I take what I hid myself –
perfume, precious and rare, never meant to spill or spare.
This I'll carefully break, this I'll empty for his sake:
I will give what I have to my Lord.

2.

Though the action is crude, it will show my gratitude
for the truth that I've learnt from the one who's heaven-sent;
for this life once a mess which his beauty can express,
I will give what I have to my Lord.

3.

With his critics around, common gossip will abound.
They'll note all that they see to discredit him and me.
Let them smirk, let them jeer, say what people want to hear;
I will give what I have to my Lord.

4.

It's because he'll receive, that the likes of me believe
God has time for the poor. He has shown us heaven's door.
Be it perfume and care, be it anger or despair,
I will give what I have to my Lord.

The act of love which this song celebrates is recorded in chapter 14 of Mark's Gospel. It is a woman's song and is best sung in the style of a French café chanson with a piano accordian accompanying. The more unaffected the voice, the more convincing the testimony.

I will sing a song of love

Tune: 'NAMED AND KNOWN', John L. Bell

LOVE OF GOD IS GOOD,_____
_____ IT IS BROAD AND DEEP AND LONG,_____ AND A-
BOVE ALL ELSE THAT MAT - TERS GOD IS_____
WOR - THY_____ OF MY SONG._____

D   C/D
Bm7   Gm6/B♭
D/A   G   Bm
Em7   A7   D

Fine

Verse 1

And I will not sing a-lone_____ but with earth and sky and sea,

Gmaj7 A7/G F#m Bm Em7 F# Bm

_____ for cre - a - tion raised its

G A7/G

voice well in ad - vance of me.

D.C.

D/F# Bm Gm7 C7 F A7

Chorus:
I WILL SING A SONG OF LOVE
TO THE ONE WHO FIRST LOVED ME,
AND I'LL SING IT AS A CHILD OF GOD,
WHO IS NAMED AND KNOWN AND FREE.
FOR THE LOVE OF GOD IS GOOD,
IT IS BROAD AND DEEP AND LONG;
AND ABOVE ALL ELSE THAT MATTERS,
GOD IS WORTHY OF MY SONG.

1.
And I will not sing alone
but with earth and sky and sea,
for creation raised its voice
well in advance of me.

2.
And I'll sing with every soul,
every language, every race,
which proclaims this world is good
for God has blessed this place.

3.
And I'll sing for what is right
and against all that is wrong,
because God is never neutral
who inspires my song.

4.
As I bring to God my joy,
so I'll bring to God my pain
for there is no hurt which God
requires me to retain.

5.
While my life on earth still runs,
may my song to God be given,
till through grace I join the harmony
of all in heaven.

This song is a testimony both to the love of God and to the breadth of praise which is offered in response to that love. It is the antithesis of the smug, egocentric 'me and Jesus' praise song which – in the face of biblical testimony – denies the importance to God of the voice of creation, and encourages the false presumption that worship is synonymous with good feelings.

He is the Way

Music: John L. Bell

36

You will see rare beasts and have u-

You will come to a great ci-ty that has ex-

nique ad-ven-tures.

pect-ed your re-turn for years.

Swell

subito

Choir

WORLD OF THE FLESH AND AT YOUR MAR - RIAGE ALL ITS OC-

FLESH_____

CA - SIONS SHALL DANCE FOR JOY.

Great

1.
He is the Way.
Follow him through the land of unlikeness.
You will see rare beasts
and have unique adventures.

2.
He is the Truth.
Seek him in the kingdom of anxiety.
You will come to a great city
that has expected your return for years.

3.
He is the Life.
Love him in the world of the flesh
and at your marriage
all its occasions shall dance for joy.

Great poets do not often appear in hymnals. It seems not to be their peculiar gift or calling in the same way that not many hymn writers end up in anthologies of poetry. But sometimes the divide is crossed as in this beautiful text by W. H. Auden (1907-73), from 'The Flight Into Egypt' section of the long poem, 'For The Time Being' (A Christmas Oratio). Its inspiration is the saying of Jesus, 'I am the Way, the Truth and the Life.' This setting was written for the wedding of Alison Adam and Martyn Coe in December 2001.

Jesus Christ, here among us

Tune: 'VIA, VERITAS, VITA', John L. Bell

Gently but firmly ♩ = *60*

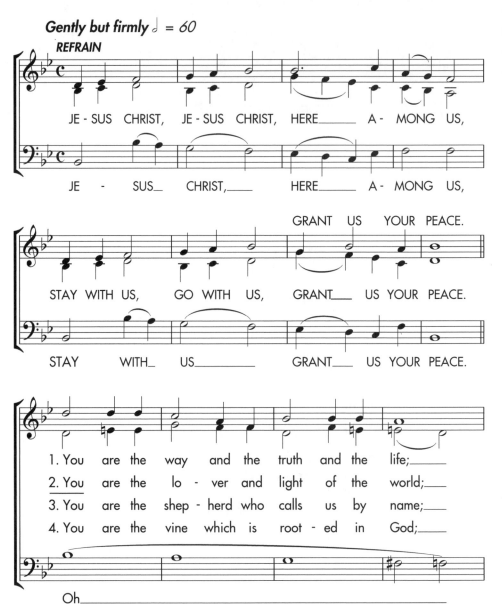

REFRAIN

JE - SUS CHRIST, JE - SUS CHRIST, HERE____ A - MONG US,

JE - SUS__ CHRIST,____ HERE____ A - MONG US,

GRANT US YOUR PEACE.

STAY WITH US, GO WITH US, GRANT____ US YOUR PEACE.

STAY WITH__ US_____ GRANT____ US YOUR PEACE.

1. You are the way and the truth and the life;____
2. You are the lo - ver and light of the world;____
3. You are the shep - herd who calls us by name;____
4. You are the vine which is root - ed in God;____

Oh_____

Words & music John L. Bell, copyright © 2005 WGRG, Iona Community, Glasgow G2 3DH, Scotland.

in you the full - ness of God is found.____
ev - en the dark - ness is light to you.____
none who res - pond will be turned a - way.____
graft - ed to you we will bear much fruit.____

Oh_____

Refrain:
JESUS CHRIST, JESUS CHRIST, HERE AMONG US
GO WITH US, STAY WITH US,
GRANT US YOUR PEACE.

1.
You are the way and the truth and the life;
in you the fullness of God is found.

2.
You are the lover and light of the world;
even the darkness is light to you.

3.
You are the shepherd who calls us by name;
none who respond will be turned away.

4.
You are the vine which is rooted in God;
grafted to you we will bear much fruit.

This simple three-part evening song alludes to the many names by which Christ is known. These titles are not the colours of a chameleon, but evidence of a kaleidoscopic personality which we will never fully understand this side of time.

A cradling song

Tune: 'JENNIFER', John L. Bell

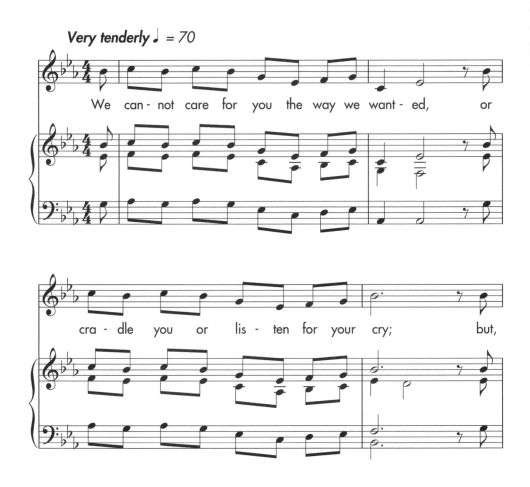

We can-not care for you the way we want-ed, or

cra - dle you or lis - ten for your cry; but,

sep - a - ra - ted   as   we   are   by   si - lence,

1. - 4.　　　　　　　　　　　　　**5.**

love will not die.　　　breathes with your breath.

44

1.

We cannot care for you the way we wanted,
or cradle you or listen for your cry;
but, separated as we are by silence,
love will not die.

2.

We cannot watch you grow into childhood
and find a new uniqueness every day –
but special as you would have been among us,
you still will stay.

3.

We cannot know the pain or the potential
which passing years would summon or reveal;
but for that true fulfilment Jesus promised
we hope and feel.

4.

So through the mess of anger, grief and tiredness,
through tensions which are not yet reconciled,
we give to God the worship of our sorrow
and our dear child.

5.

Lord, in your arms which cradle all creation
we rest and place our baby beyond death,
believing that she now, alive in heaven,
breathes with your breath.

Based on the witness of a young couple whose baby survived for only a few minutes, this song is intended for use at funerals or remembrance services for prenatal deaths. It is best be sung solo, or alternatively the words may be spoken over the chordal accompaniment. For the benefit of the bereft and their friends, it may be helpful to have the text printed for all to follow.

In this darkness

Tune: *'BRIDGE OF WAITING'*, John L. Bell

Slowly and gently ♩ = 60

1. In this dark - ness I do not ask to walk by___ light;
2. In this si - lence I do not ask to hear your___ voice;
3. In un - know - ing I do not ask for fear - less___ space;
4. In this death___ I do not ask to for - feit___ pain,

but to feel the touch of your hand and
but to sense your Spi - rit___ breathe and
but for grace to com - pre - hend that
but to gain the strength to___ love through

un - der - stand that sight is not see - ing.
so be - queathe my care to your keep - ing.
neith - er you nor I are di - min - ished.
loss and cross the bridge of___ wait - ing.

1.
In this darkness
I do not ask to walk by light;
but to feel the touch of your hand
and understand that sight is not seeing.

2.
In this silence
I do not ask to hear your voice;
but to sense your Spirit breathe
and so bequeath my care to your keeping.

3.
In unknowing
I do not ask for fearless space;
but for grace to comprehend
that neither you nor I are diminished.

4.
In this death
I do not ask to forfeit pain,
but to gain the strength to love
through loss, and cross the bridge of waiting.   *(notes overleaf)*

The original poem:

In this darkness
I do not ask to walk by light;
but to feel the touch of your hand
and understand that sight is not seeing.

In this silence
I do not ask to hear your voice;
but to sense your Spirit breathe
and know myself a word of your speaking.

In unknowing
I do not ask for fearless space;
but for grace to comprehend
that neither you or I are diminished.
In this death
I do not seek escape from pain;
but embracing loss, to find
the strength to cross the bridge of waiting.

This song developed from the poem (printed above) by Pat Bennett. As with paraphrases of scripture, it is not possible for the song to represent every nuance of the original text, but the poem sentiments seemed so unique and worth a wider audience. We are grateful to Pat for her permission to re-work her text.

If the war goes on

Tune: 'ROAD TO BASRA', John L. Bell

wo - men learn how to dance with - out a part - ner; who will

Gm7   C   Fmaj7   Bb

keep the score?

Gm7   A   Gm7   A

1.
If the war goes on
and the children die of hunger,
and the old men weep
for the young men are no more,
and the women learn
how to dance without a partner
who will keep the score?

(continued)

2.
If the war goes on
and the truth is taken hostage;
and new horrors lead
to the need to euphemise,
when the calls for peace
are declared unpatriotic,
who'll expose the lies?

3.
If the war goes on
and the daily bread is terror,
and the voiceless poor
take the road as refugees;
when a nation's pride
destines millions to be homeless,
who will heed their pleas?

4.
If the war goes on
and the rich increase their fortunes
and the arms sales soar
as new weapons are displayed,
when a fertile field
turns to no-man's-land tomorrow,
who'll approve such trade?

5.
If the war goes on
will we close the doors to heaven,
if the war goes on,
will we breach the gates of hell;
if the war goes on,
will we ever be forgiven,
if the war goes on ... and on ... and on ...?

Somewhere in the middle of the 20th century, Western Christians lost the ability to lament. It may be attributed to a false sense of security and self righteousness during the Cold War; it may have been the corrosive acid of easy theology which proclaimed that God could only deal with the positives and that if bad things happened it was the result of undischarged guilt. What happened to the just anger and cries of protest that inhabited Dylan and Baez in the sixties and that fuelled the fervour of the civil rights movement? How sad that the late 20th and early 21st century Anglo-American incursions into the Gulf and hyper-cautiousness regarding the Israel–Palestine conflict should find no response in the Church's song.

I heard the voice of Jesus say

Tune: 'THE ROWAN TREE', Scots traditional

Moderato ♩ = 60

1. I_ heard the voice of Je-sus say, 'Come un-to me and
2. I_ heard the voice of Je-sus say, 'Be-hold, I free-ly
3. I_ heard the voice of Je-sus say, 'I am this dark world's

C   F/C

rest;_____ lay____ down, thou wea - ry
give_____ the____ liv - ing wa - ter,
light;_____ look____ un - to me, thy

C

one, lay down thy head up - on my breast':
thir - sty one, stoop down and drink and live':
morn shall rise, and all thy day be bright':

F/C   C   G7   C

Words Horatius Bonar (1808–89). Arrangement John L. Bell, copyright © 2005 WGRG, Iona Community, Glasgow G2 3DH, Scotland.

1.

I heard the voice of Jesus say,
'Come unto me and rest;
lay down, thou weary one, lay down
thy head upon my breast:
I came to Jesus as I was,
so weary and worn and sad;
I found in him a resting-place,
and he has made me glad.

2.

I heard the voice of Jesus say,
'Behold, I freely give
the living water, thirsty one,
stoop down and drink and live':
I came to Jesus, and I drank
of that life-giving stream;
my thirst was quenched, my soul revived
and now I live in him.

3.

I heard the voice of Jesus say,
'I am this dark world's light;
look unto me, thy morn shall rise,
and all thy day be bright':
I looked to Jesus, and I found
in him my star, my sun;
and in that light of life I'll walk
till travelling days are done.

The Scottish churches have not always encouraged artistic creativity, as the author of this world-renowned text knew well. Horatius Bonar (1808-89) was a Presbyterian minister the elders in whose Edinburgh congregation would not allow his hymns to be sung at public worship. It would have been equally repugnant for them to contemplate a religious text being sung to a native folk tune (though Irish, English and Welsh melodies seemed to escape censure). What a loss, especially since 'The Rowan Tree' so aptly suits the words, particularly if this song of testimony has the first half of each verse sung solo.

Hey my love

Tune: 'LADY MAISRY', Scots traditional

1. Blessed are the ones_ I_____ call the poor, hey my love and ho my joy; blessed are the ones_____ I_____ call the poor, who dear-ly love me; blessed are the ones I call the poor: the king-dom is their own for sure:

REFRAIN

GOD'S KING-DOM IS OF HEA-VEN, OF EARTH, OF FIRE, OF LOVE.

1.
Blessed are the ones I call the poor,
HEY MY LOVE AND HO MY JOY;
blessed are the ones I call the poor
WHO DEARLY LOVE ME.
Blessed are the ones I call the poor:
the kingdom is their own for sure.

Refrain:
GOD'S KINGDOM IS OF HEAVEN,
OF EARTH, OF FIRE, OF LOVE.

2.
Blessed are the ones who deeply mourn...
God's comfort in their hearts is known.

3.
Blessed are the ones who gently care...
they'll have the whole wide world to share.

4.
Blessed are the ones who thirst for right...
their journey's end is filled with light.

5.
Blessed are the ones who pardon all...
they'll be forgiven when they call.

6.
Blessed are the ones whose pure hearts shine...
they'll see their Lord and with him dine.

7.
Blessed are the ones who work for peace....
as God's own children they'll increase.

8.
Blessed are the ones the world puts down...
they'll have the kingdom for their own,   *(note overleaf)*

The Eastern Orthodox Church, to which the ancient Celtic church was linked, has always sung the Beatitudes – the eight statements of Jesus which characterise those who are truly blessed. Here the Scottish east coast folk tune 'Lady Maisry' allows for a meditative rendering of the passage in St Matthew's Gospel.

I am the Vine

Tune: 'VINE AND BRANCHES', John L. Bell

Moderato ♩ = 84

mf I AM THE VINE AND YOU THE BRAN - CHES,

PRUNED AND PRE - PARED FOR ALL___ TO SEE;

CHO - SEN TO BEAR THE FRUIT OF HEA - VEN

SA - VOUR THAT LOVE___ WHICH NE - VER DIES.

mp Though as a ser - vant to you I came,

Though, though as a ser - vant to you I

Though as a ser - vant to you I came,

Though as a ser - vant to you I

you are not sum - moned to bear that name.

came,___ you're not___ to bear that name.___

you are not sum - moned to bear___ that name.

came,___ you're not to bear that name.

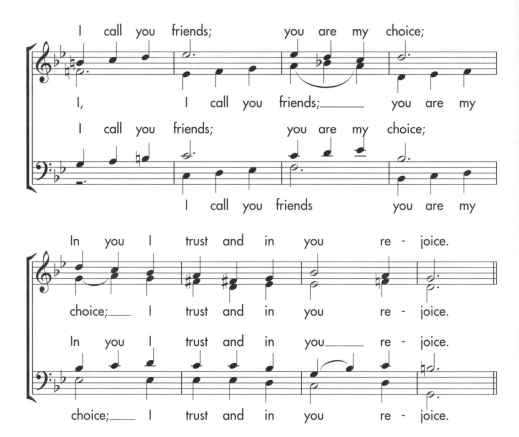

STAY CLOSE AND ROOT MY WORDS WITH - IN YOU:

WHAT YOU RE - QUEST,___ YOU SOON___ SHALL HAVE___

UN - TIL YOU CAR - RY FRUIT IN PLEN - TY,

NOU - RISHED AND FER - TILE THROUGH_ MY LOVE.

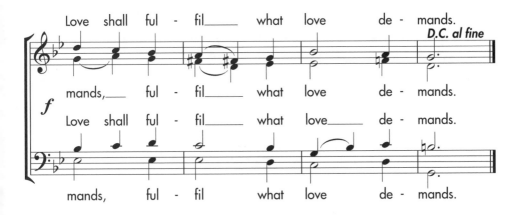

1.
I am the Vine and you the branches,
pruned and prepared for all to see;
chosen to bear the fruit of heaven
if you remain and trust in me.
For on your own, what can you bear?
Left to yourself no sap you share:
branches that serve their own desire
find themselves broken as fuel for fire.

2.
So let my joy complete and cheer you
in whom my hope and kingdom lies;
loving each other as I loved you,
savour that love which never dies.
Though as a servant to you I came,
you are not summoned to bear that name.
I call you friends; you are my choice;
in you I trust and in you rejoice.

(continued)

3.
Stay close and root my words within you:
what you request you soon shall have
until you carry fruit in plenty,
nourished and fertile through my love.
    In this is glory given to God
    <u>as</u> you, my <u>chosen ones, prove my word</u>:
    gladly <u>obedient to my commands</u>,
    love shall <u>fulfil what love demands</u>.

4.
I am the Vine and you the branches,
pruned and prepared for all to see;
chosen to bear the fruit of heaven
if you remain and trust in me.

John chapter 15 (v 1-10) is the Gospel passage on which this anthem is based. It may be sung antiphonally by a choir and congregation, with the choir singing the second half of each verse.

Note: The underlined words are the only ones sung in the requisite lines by alto and bass. The words which are boldest type are sung twice by alto.

72 O Jesus, sweet the thought of you

Tune: 'SONDYSAM', John L. Bell

1.
O Jesus, sweet the thought of you
which fills my yearning heart;
but sweeter is your company
and it will not depart.

2.
No voice can sing, no ear can hear,
no thought can bring to mind
a sweeter sound than Jesus' name
God's gift to humankind.

3.
O Jesus, hope of guilty folk
who long to be forgiven,
you welcome all who question you
and seek a glimpse of heaven.

4.
And what are you to those who find?
No pen no tongue can tell
what Jesus' love is like: they know
in whom you choose to dwell.

5.
O Jesus, be our deepest joy
our glory and our prize,
until in heaven we see ourselves
and all things through your eyes.

Love songs to Jesus are no new invention. This text is over a thousand years old. It comes from a longer poem entitled 'Jesu Dulcis Memoria" which is forty two stanzas long and was previously attributed to Bernard of Clairvaux. Though the authorship is now disputed, the directness, affection and intimacy in the text is unrivalled.

Mothering God

Tune: 'JULIAN', John L. Bell.

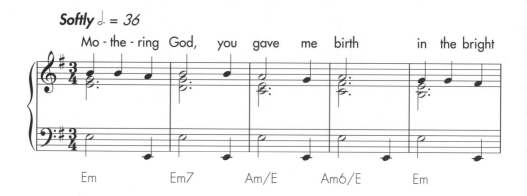

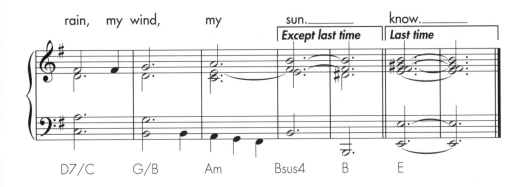

1.
Mothering God, you gave me birth
in the bright morning of the world.
Creator, Source of every breath,
you are my rain, my wind, my sun;
you are my rain, my wind, my sun.

2.
Mothering Christ, you took my form,
offering me your food of light,
grain of life and grape of love,
your very body for my peace;
your very body for my peace.

3.
Mothering Spirit, nurturing one,
in arms of patience hold me close,
so that in faith I root and grow
until I flower, until I know;
until I flower, until I know.

Julian of Norwich, the 14th century English anchoress and mystic, is at last coming of age. Her musing on revelations of divine love includes the profound scriptural insight that God cannot be spoken of solely in male terms.

This text is a contemporary rendering of Julian's words by the American poet Jean Janzen. When the Mennonite church, seeking to set the words to music, offered the text to composers, nearly all responses were pitched in the key of E or E minor. Is this the mothering tone?

The mind of God

Tune: 'WARRICK', John L. Bell

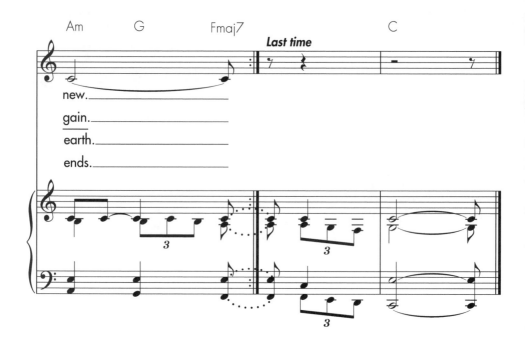

1.
The mind of God is forever changing,
forever pondering what shall yet come true,
forever noting every child's potential,
forever restless to make all things new.

2.
The heart of God is forever changing,
forever moved by each cry of pain,
forever touched when we say we're sorry,
forever yearning that we start again.

3.
The world God made is forever changing,
forever moving between death and birth,
forever turning through the seasons' cycle,
forever clothing the productive earth.

4.
The love of God – this is never changing,
but brings to light all that God intends;
transforming those who are met by Jesus,
the love of God never, ever ends.

One of the eternal conundrums of the Christian faith is the changelessness of God. Some Christians take umbrage if it suggested that anything to do with God might show evidence of change. Yet in the Old Testament God repeatedly 'repents' or has a change of heart, and in the New Testament, Christ comes in order that nothing and no one will remain the same. We have to decide – is God dynamic or inert? This song reflects on such issues.

Alphabetical index of first lines and titles

(Where different, titles are shown in italics)

The Iona Community

The Iona Community, founded in 1938 by the Revd George MacLeod, then a parish minister in Glasgow, is an ecumenical Christian community committed to seeking new ways of living the Gospel in today's world. Initially working to restore part of the medieval abbey on Iona, the Community today remains committed to 'rebuilding the common life' through working for social and political change, striving for the renewal of the church with an ecumenical emphasis, and exploring new, more inclusive approaches to worship, all based on an integrated understanding of spirituality.

The Community now has over 240 Members, about 1500 Associate Members and around 1500 Friends. The Members – women and men from many denominations and backgrounds (lay and ordained), living throughout Britain with a few overseas – are committed to a fivefold Rule of devotional discipline, sharing and accounting for use of time and money, regular meeting, and action for justice and peace.

At the Community's three residential centres – the Abbey and the MacLeod Centre on Iona, and Camas Adventure Camp on the Ross of Mull – guests are welcomed from March to October and over Christmas. Hospitality is provided for over 110 people, along with a unique opportunity, usually through week-long programmes, to extend horizons and forge relationships through sharing an experience of the common life in worship, work, discussion and relaxation. The Community's shop on Iona, just outside the Abbey grounds, carries an attractive range of books and craft goods.

The Community's administrative headquarters are in Glasgow, which also serves as a base for its work with young people, the Wild Goose Resource Group working in the field of worship, a bi-monthly magazine, *Coracle*, and a publishing house, Wild Goose Publications.

For information on the Iona Community contact:
The Iona Community
Fourth Floor, Savoy House,
140 Sauchiehall Street, Glasgow G2 3DH, UK
Phone: 0141 332 6343   e-mail: ionacomm@gla.iona.org.uk
web: www.iona.org.uk

For enquiries about visiting Iona, please contact:
Iona Abbey, Isle of Iona, Argyll PA76 6SN, UK
Phone: 01681 700404   e-mail: ionacomm@iona.org.uk

The Wild Goose Resource and Worship Groups

The Wild Goose Resource Group is an expression of the Iona Community's commitment to the renewal of public worship. Based in Glasgow, the WGRG has two resource workers, John Bell and Graham Maule, who lead workshops, seminars and events throughout Britain and abroad. They are supported by Gail Ullrich (administrator), Victoria Rudebark (sales & copyright administrator).

From 1984 to 2001, the WGRG workers were also part of the Wild Goose Worship Group. The WGWG consisted of around sixteen, predominantly lay, people at any one time, who came from a variety of occupational and denominational backgrounds. Over the 17 years of its existence, it was the WGWG who tested, as well as promoted, the material in this book.

The task of both groups has been to develop and identify new methods and materials to enable the revitalisation of congregational song, prayer and liturgy. The songs and liturgical material have now been translated and used in many countries across the world as well as being frequently broadcast on radio and television.

The WGRG, along with a committed group of fellow-Glaswegians, run HOLY CITY, a monthly ecumenical workshop and worship event for adults in the centre of Glasgow. The WGRG also publishes a mail-order catalogue, an annual Liturgy Booklet series and a twice-yearly newsletter, GOOSEgander, to enable friends and supporters to keep abreast of WGRG developments. If you would like to find out more about subscribing to these, or about ways to support the WGRG financially, please contact:

The Wild Goose Resource Group
Iona Community
Fourth Floor, Savoy House
140 Sauchiehall Street
Glasgow G2 3DH, Scotland.
Tel: 0141 332 6343   Fax: 0141 332 1090
e-mail: wgrg@gla.iona.org.uk
web: www.iona.org.uk/wgrg.html

Also from the Wild Goose Resource Group . . .

I WILL NOT SING ALONE — CD
John L. Bell, The Wild Goose Collective & Macappella

John L. Bell and Graham Maule of the Wild Goose Resource group join with a diverse collection of musicians to sing the songs in this book. The Wild Goose Collective are an ad hoc collection of ex-Wild Goose Worship Group members and other colleagues. The Macappella Ceilidh Band are based in Glasgow and have close connections with the Iona Community.

CD • ISBN 1 901557 89 8

ONE IS THE BODY – CD & SONGBOOK
The Wild Goose Worship Group

A new collection of songs from many countries along with new ones from John L. Bell and Graham Maule. 'We do not believe that it is any longer possible to claim membership of the "holy catholic Church" and refuse to sing songs from the repertoire of the mission-sending churches in the North. If we do not share the gifts of Asian, African and Latin American Christians, our grandchildren will regard us as racist.'

CD • ISBN 1 901557 37 5
Songbook • ISBN 1 901557 35 9

THERE IS ONE AMONG US: Shorter songs for worship — CD & SONGBOOK
The Wild Goose Worship Group

Simple yet richly rewarding wee songs from the Wild Goose Worship Group which can be used in a variety of situations from cathedrals to classrooms, open air festivals to in-house groups. Excellent for innovative and participatory styles of workshop. Songbook also gives helpful hints on using the material and includes an appendix of new readings and prayers for use with the songs.

CD • ISBN 1 901557 21 9
Songbook • ISBN 1 901557 10 3

THE SINGING THING: A case for congregational song
John L. Bell

One of the world's experts on congregational song writes for those who want to encourage others to sing or sing better. He offers ten persuasive answers to the question 'Why do we sing?' Each answer is explored with a wealth of practical insight born of the author's twenty years of experience in this field.

ISBN 1 901557 28 6

STATES OF BLISS AND YEARNING: The marks and means of authentic Christian spirituality
John L. Bell

Spirituality is not a permanent high, a continual blissed-out state. To experience the heights, one has also to know the depths. In these sermons and addresses dealing with diverse issues from private devotion to public debt, the picture of God that emerges is one of a compassionate being who asks that we do only what we can, starting from where we are, to be just and compassionate too.

ISBN 1 901557 07 3

SONGBOOKS/OCTAVOS/CDs

Come All You People (bk/CD), John L. Bell   ISBN 0 947988 68 8/1 901557 40 5
Courage to Say No (bk/CD), John L. Bell/Graham Maule   ISBN 0 947988 78 5/
1 901557 44 8
Enemy of Apathy (bk), John L. Bell/Graham Maule   ISBN 0 947988 270
God Never Sleeps (oct/CD), John L. Bell   ISBN 0 941050 82 3/0 941050 80 7
Heaven Shall Not Wait (bk/CD), John L. Bell/Graham Maule   ISBN 1 901557 80 4/
1 901557 45 6
Innkeepers and Lightsleepers (bk/CD), John L.Bell   ISBN 0 947988 47 5/1 901557 39 1
Last Journey (bk/oct/CD), John L. Bell   ISBN 0 947988 94 7/0 947988 95 5/
0 947988 93 9
Love and Anger (bk/CD), John Bell/Graham Maule   ISBN 0 947988 98 X/1 901577 41 3
Love From Below (bk/CD), John L. Bell/Graham Maule   ISBN 0 947988 34 3/
1 901557 46 4
Many and Great (bk/CD), John L. Bell (ed./arr.)   ISBN 0 947988 40 8/1 901557 42 1
Psalms Patience Protest Praise (bk/CD), John L. Bell   ISBN 0 947988 56 4/0 947988 57 2
Sent By the Lord (bk/CD), John L. Bell (ed./arr.)   ISBN 0 947988 44 0/1 901557 43 X
Seven Psalms of David (octavos), John L. Bell   ISBN 1 579990 22 3
Seven Songs of Mary (book), John L. Bell   ISBN 1 579990 20 7
Seven Songs Mary /7 Psalms David (CD), John L. Bell   ISBN 1 579990 21 5
Take This Moment (oct/CD),John L. Bell   ISBN 1 901557 47 2/1 901557 34 0
When Grief is Raw (bk), John L.Bell/Graham Maule   ISBN 0 947988 91 2

RESOURCE BOOKS

Cloth for the Cradle (bk), Wild Goose Worship Group   ISBN 1 901557 01 4
He Was in the World, John L. Bell   ISBN 0 947988 70 X
Jesus & Peter, John L. Bell/Graham Maule   ISBN 1 901557 17 0
Present On Earth, Wild Goose Worship Group   ISBN 1 901557 64 2
Stages on the Way, Wild Goose Worship Group   ISBN 1 901557 11 1
Wee Worship Book, Wild Goose Worship Group   ISBN 1 901557 19 7

Wild Goose Publications, the publishing house of the Iona Community established in the Celtic Christian tradition of St Columba, produces books, tapes and CDs on:

- holistic spirituality
- social justice
- political and peace issues
- healing
- innovative approaches to worship
- song in worship, including the work of the Wild Goose Resource Group
- material for meditation and reflection

If you would like to find out more about our books, tapes and CDs, please contact us at:

Wild Goose Publications
Fourth Floor, Savoy House
140 Sauchiehall Street,
Glasgow G2 3DH, UK

Tel. +44 (0)141 332 6292
Fax +44 (0)141 332 1090
e-mail: admin@ionabooks.com

or visit our website at
www.ionabooks.com
for details of all our products and online sales